TION VAN
ITIAL SION A...

SNOWBALL M... ... FIRE!

EQUIPMENT EFFECTIVENESS:
Speed
Stealth
Firepower

VERTICAL MISSION!

EQUIPMENT EFFECTIVENESS:
Speed
Stealth
Firepower

MOUNTAIN MISSION!

EQUIPMENT EFFECTIVENESS:
Speed
Stealth
Firepower

ACTION MAN ANNUAL 2003

CONTENTS

SPECIAL AGENT DATA INFORMATION

Name: Unknown
Code name: Action Man
Height: 185cm
Weight: 76kg
Distinguishing features:
Scar on cheek

Specialist skills: (rating 1-5)

Skill	Rating
Combat	★ ★ ★ ★ ★
Weaponry	★ ★ ★ ★ ★
Navigation	★ ★ ★ ★ ★
Communication	★ ★ ★ ★ ★
Computer	★ ★ ★ ★ ★
Martial Arts	★ ★ ★ ★ ★
Endurance	★ ★ ★ ★ ★

Any additional info:
A multi talented and skilled agent whose prime objective is to bring the evil Council of Doom crushing to its knees.

Join Action Man in helping rid the world of the Council of Doom – but first, make sure you fill in your own Cadet details below:

Cadet profile

Stick a photograph of yourself here!

Specialist skills: (rating 1-5)

Skill	Rating
Combat	★ ★ ★ ★ ★
Weaponry	★ ★ ★ ★ ★
Navigation	★ ★ ★ ★ ★
Communication	★ ★ ★ ★ ★
Computer	★ ★ ★ ★ ★
Martial Arts	★ ★ ★ ★ ★
Endurance	★ ★ ★ ★ ★

Name:
Code name:
Height:
Weight:
Distinguishing features:

Any additional info:

Pedigree

Published by Pedigree Books Limited
The Old Rectory, Matford Lane, Exeter EX2 4PS
E-mail: books@pedigreegroup.co.uk
Published in 2002

Licensed by:

Consumer Products

©2002 Hasbro International Inc.
All rights reserved.

£6.99

NINJITSU EXTREME!

MISSION BRIEF: *Special intelligence data recently received has revealed that the Council of Doom are about to unleash a global plot to take over the world. Action Man must be sent to investigate ...IMMEDIATELY! He'll be going in with the following mission equipment...*

SPECIAL OPERATION EQUIPMENT:

ROTATING SABRE

• The blades of this lightweight fighting tool can cut through the toughest materials. When activated and in attack mode, the blades can be rotated at the flick of a switch. Another switch enables the blades to be retracted back into the central handle.

FOREARM STABILIZER

• A reinforced forearm protector gives extra strength, support and protection to Action Man's fighting arm.

HEADGEAR

• A small, lightweight radio receiver and transmitter is hidden beneath Action Man's Ninja headband. A hands-free microphone is attached to the receiver for ease of communication.

SHOULDER HARNESS

• The rotating sabre is stored in this shoulder harness – ensuring that it is always within easy reach.

MISSION LOCATION:

KONUKU TEMPLE, KONUKU, JAPAN

• THIS ANCIENT JAPANESE TEMPLE IS UNDER THREAT FROM THE COUNCIL OF DOOM

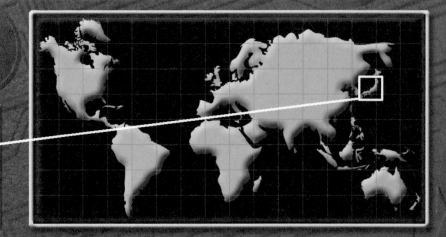

SOON, DR X'S THUGS ARE RIPPING THE PLACE APART!

ZZHHWAAAKKK!

THE POWER OF MY LIGHTNING BOLTS WILL TRASH THIS PLACE! HA-HA!

NOT IF I CAN HELP IT, TEMPEST!

HUH?

THWAK!

OH-NO! IT'S ACTION MAN! HE MUST BE DESTROYED!

THE STORY CONTINUES ON PAGE 27!

COLOUR-UP!

OPERATION: PERILOUS PATHWAY!

Help retrace Action Man's steps into the ancient Japanese temple by guiding him through this mind-blowing maze. Be careful not to run into any 'fighting star' booby traps on the way!

start

MISSION DEBRIEF: THE KEYS TO INFINITY

Test your special agent skills by trying to answer as many questions as possible about the preceding story: THE KEYS TO INFINITY. When you've finished check your answers at the foot of this page. Then calculate your score and see how you have been rated by Action Man.

1. Where did Action Man's adventure begin?
a. Japan
b. Turkey
c. America

2. What type of equipment did Action Man take on his mission?
a. Vertical Mission
b. Ninjitsu Extreme
c. Windsurfer Extreme

3. How was the Council of Doom planning to take over the world?
a. By holding up a series of banks
b. By opening and unleashing the power from the 'Keyholes to Infinity'
c. By building a super-charged laser

4. What type of machine was used to attack Action Man during his mission?
a. A tank
b. A helicopter
c. A bulldozer with a giant ball

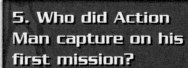

5. Who did Action Man capture on his first mission?
a. Dr X
b. Gangrene
c. Tempest

HOW YOU RATED:

5 answers correct: Top marks! What an exellent performance. You can proceed to the next mission with flying colours!

2-4 answers correct: A good start – but if you want to improve you'll need to sharpen your vision in the next mission.

0-1 answer correct: Oh, dear! Did you even read the first mission?

ENTER THE C

Are you really brave enough to find out more about the Council of Doom and what makes them tick? Well, don't say you haven't been warned...

Profile: Evil to the core. Will stop at nothing to defeat Action Man. Used to be a lone criminal aspiring for world domination – but has now built an alliance with Gangrene and Tempest.

Favourite phrase: This time next year the world will be mine! Ha-ha-ha!

Likes: Watching Action Man squirm, holding the world to ransom and cackling like a madman!

Dislikes: Being defeated (which happens a lot!)

BAD GUY1

DR. X

PERSONAL DATA:

Metal head plate:
Fused with Dr X's brain, this protective head-plate also has an eye-piece that can magnify distant objects and enhance night-vision.

Body armour:
Dr X's chest-plate protector can repel all firepower and withstand the toughest blows.

Robotic arm:
Hydraulically operated - can lift up to four tonnes and smash rocks to pieces. Four miniature missiles fire from handset.

DANGER RATING: 10/10

Profile: A toxic time-bomb just waiting to explode. Loves to experiment with new poisonous substances and then unleash them on the unexpecting.

Favourite phrase: Oooh – I think I've got a virus!
Likes: Anything toxic.
Dislikes: Anything that isn't toxic.

BAD GUY 2

PROF.
GANGRENE

PERSONAL DATA:

Sludge gun:

Gangrene's weapon is able to propel toxic fluid and gases up to 200 metres.

Toxic generator:

A reservoir within Gangrene's body suit enables rapid production of toxins and viruses.

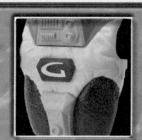

Head control unit:

The controls on Gangrene's headset allow him to adjust the intensity of toxic fluid he concocts in his generator.

DANGER RATING: 10/10

Profile: This guy aims to shock! Has a very short fuse but makes up for it with his electric personality. When fully charged he can blow anyone's lights out!

Favourite phrase: Power – up!
Likes: Re-energising his body and then blasting Action Man.
Dislikes: Water – because it short-circuits his system.

PERSONAL DATA:

Combat staffs:

These weapons allow Tempest to conduct and fire up to 50,000 volts of electrical energy.

Voltage harness:

Allows Tempest to adjust the level of electrical energy that is fired from either of his two staffs.

Conductor gloves:

Protect Tempest from short-circuiting when he is conducting and discharging electrical energy.

BAD GUY 3

TEMPEST

DANGER RATING: 10/10

RECRUITING NOW!
DR X WANTS YOU!

So, you've got a burning desire to take over the world and get rid of that pesky Action Man, eh? Well good! Take this test and if you're bad-to-the-bone – then you're in!

1. Why do you want to join the Council of Doom?
a. Because I want to travel the world.
b. Because I want to be the ruler of the entire world – ha, ha, ha!
c. Because I want to change the Council of Doom into a peace-loving organisation.

2. How could the Council of Doom benefit by having you as a member?
a. I want to join your gang – 'cos they look kinda cool.
b. I can make a nice cup of tea.
c. I think the Council of Doom needs a new leader – and I'm the baddest dude around – ha,ha,ha!

3. What would you do if Action Man tried to prevent you from taking over the world?
a. Squash him in my path – ha, ha, ha!
b. I'd agree that he was probably right – and give up.
c. I'd have to deny everything - and then run away.

4. When would you be able to attend an interview at the Council of Doom's secret HQ?
a. Only on Saturday mornings – the rest of the time I'm busy flower-arranging.
b. Tuesday afternoons are good for me – can I bring my mum, too?
c. Anytime – tell me when and I'll be there.

5. Striving for world domination is hard work – how would you cope with the long hours?
a. As long as I didn't have to get up before 11am - it wouldn't be a problem.
b. I'm prepared to work as hard as it takes.
c. Do I get weekends off?

SCORES: Now add up your score and check to see if you've made the grade...
1. a – 2. b – 3. c – 1.
2. a – 2. b – 1. c – 3
3. a – 3. b – 1. c – 2.
4. a – 1. b – 2. c – 3.
5. a – 1. b – 3. c – 2.

BAD-OMETER RATING:

5-7 points
Useless! You wouldn't last five minutes in my elite gang. The Council of Doom has officially rejected your application – so there!

8-11 points
Hmmm... not bad, kid! You show signs of being bad enough to get in the gang – but you're not quite there yet. Go and perfect an evil laugh – then come back next year and try again.

12-15 points
I've got to hand it to you, kid – you're pretty mean! I wasn't even as mean as you when I was your age! So now you think you're in – right? Wrong!! You're TOO bad! It'd only be a question of time until you wanted world domination all for yourself – and I can't have that!

CADET TRAINING:1
RECONNAISSANCE

It is essential that top agents can understand maps – to locate the enemy. Follow the instructions on each map and then use your reconnaissance skills to locate the entrance to each of Dr X's hidden bases. Check how well you did at the bottom of page 25.

COASTAL:

1. Start at grid location A3 and move 2 squares West then 6 squares South, stopping for cover behind a parked truck.
2. Silently move 3 squares East, keeping cover in the undergrowth.
3. Now quickly dart 2 squares East and 2 squares North – making sure you're not spotted by X's guards.
4. Finally move 3 squares East and 1 square South – to locate Dr X's coastal base.

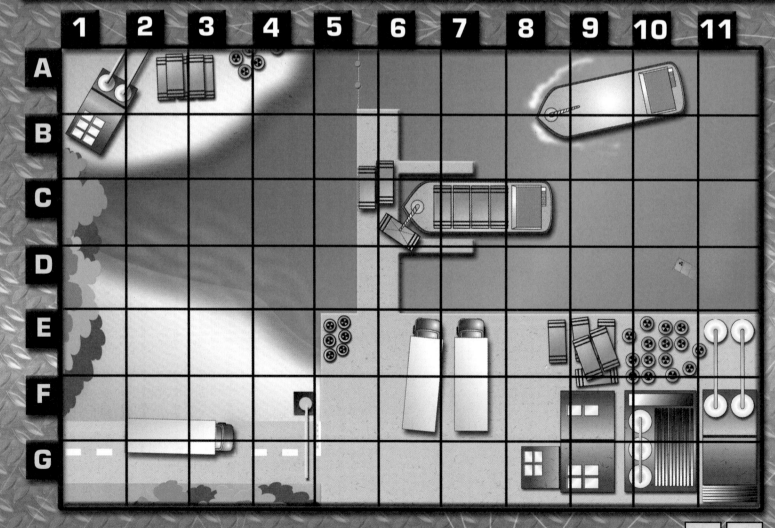

THE CO-ORDINATE FOR DR X'S COASTAL BASE IS:

INNER CITY:

1. Start at grid location B1 and move 2 squares South and 3 squares East, keeping a watchful eye out for X's men.
2. When the coast is clear, quickly head 1 square North and 3 squares East – stopping for cover in the car park.
3. Finally, continue 3 squares East and 2 squares North – to locate the entrance to Dr X's inner city headquarters.

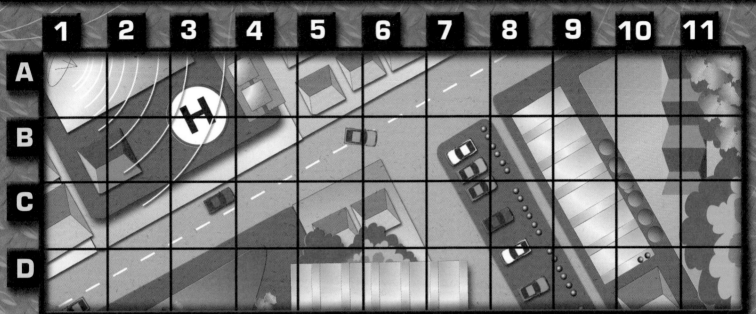

	1	2	3	4	5	6	7	8	9	10	11
A											
B											
C											
D											

THE CO-ORDINATE FOR DR X'S INNER CITY BASE IS:

INDUSTRIAL:

1. Start at grid location D8 and follow the train tracks 7 squares West.
2. Survey the area and when it's all clear head 2 squares North and 2 squares East, dropping for cover behind a factory building.
3. Now quickly race as fast as you can 5 squares East and hide behind a huge lorry.
4. Finally move 1 square North and 1 square East – and you will be facing the entrance to Dr X's Industrial hide-out.

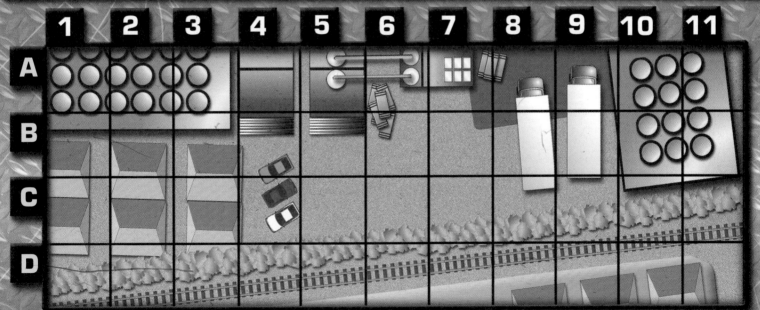

	1	2	3	4	5	6	7	8	9	10	11
A											
B											
C											
D											

THE CO-ORDINATE FOR DR X'S INDUSTRIAL BASE IS:

CADET RATING: Record the number of bases you accurately located on page 109 – to find out your overall agent rating!

MISSION DATA:

MARINE MISSION

MISSION BRIEF:
Tempest and Gangrene are still on the loose – they could show up anywhere. But we have information that leads us to believe they are heading for a swampy location in South America. Action Man needs to intercept, using the following mission equipment...

SPECIAL OPERATION EQUIPMENT:

UNDERWATER APARATUS
• The miniature, lightweight oxygen tank attached to Action Man's breathing apparatus allows him more freedom of movement.

UNDERWATER TORPEDOES
• High velocity underwater mini-torpedoes can be detonated at the press of a button. They are accurate in any water conditions up to 2 miles. Torpedoes can also be used on land – with pinpoint accuracy up to 3 miles.

DOLPHIN HARNESS
• The lightweight body harness is made from medium density latex – ensuring the dolphin's manoeuvrability is not hindered. Controllable, powerful jets of water can be dispersed from the top of the harness. Hand grips allow Action Man to ride on the dolphin's back.

DOLPHIN
• Action Man's dolphin has been highly trained by special intelligence and underwater aquatic experts. The dolphin has been trained to work in a partnership with Action Man.

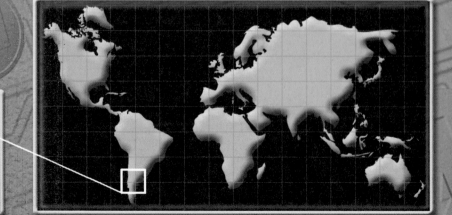

MISSION LOCATION:
COLÓNIAS, SOUTH AMERICA
HOMELAND TO ONE OF THE OLDEST TRIBES OF PEOPLE IN THE WORLD... THE MAÑITAS

UH-OH! CHANGE ONE TO FOUR. NOW I NEED TO THINK OF A PLAN... FAST!

HEY! LET ME PUT MY OXYGEN MASK ON!

THIS DOLPHIN SURE KNOWS ALL THE BEST MOVES!

SWOOOOSSSH!

AND STILL THEY COME - I THINK IT'S TIME TO GET OUT OF HERE!

WE MUST GO DEEPER. WE DON'T WANT THOSE THUGS TRYING TO HARPOON US!

ELSEWHERE. TEMPEST MAKES HIS SNEAKY ESCAPE...

OKAY! SO ACTION MAN WON THIS BATTLE. BUT NEXT TIME I'M GONNA FRY HIM LIKE A SAUSAGE!

MUCH, MUCH LATER... THE MANITAS ARE GLAD TO RETURN HOME.

AND A SHORT AIRCRAFT JOURNEY LATER...

LOOK ON THE BRIGHT SIDE, GANGRENE. YOU'RE ABOUT TO BE REUNITED WITH AN OLD FRIEND!

GAHH! YOU'LL PAY FOR THIS ACTION MAN!

BUT THIS IS ONE RE-UNION THAT DOESN'T GO TO PLAN!

THWAK!

BUT IT WASN'T MY FAULT, DR X - HONEST!!

GANGRENE! YOU HAVE FAILED THE COUNCIL OF DOOM, AGAIN!

THE STORY CONTINUES ON PAGE 41!

OPERATION: SUPER SEA-SEARCH!

During Action Man's adventure with his Marine Mission dolphin, he spotted lots of things in the sea. Take a look at the list below – then try and find them in the word-grid. Names can be spelt forwards, backwards or diagonally.

D	I	W	T	C	O	R	A	L	L
Q	R	S	A	N	B	A	N	O	
S	H	I	P	W	R	E	C	K	
Y	E	J	F	X	E	O	H	R	
F	G	E	N	T	C	H	O	A	
I	K	I	L	C	W	V	R	H	
S	U	P	O	T	C	O	D	S	
H	M	R	E	T	S	B	O	L	
B	C	R	A	B	P	F	L	D	

Octopus **Shipwreck** **Lobster**

Shark

Crab **Fish** **Anchor**

Eel **Driftwood** **Coral**

MISSION DEBRIEF: THE LOST CITY

Test your special agent skills by trying to answer as many questions as possible about the preceding story: **THE LOST CITY**. When you've finished. check your answers at the foot of this page. Then calculate your score to see how you have been rated by Action Man.

1. Where was Dr X imprisoned?
a. Fort Knox
b. Demon's Island
c. Parkhurst prison

2. Where did Action Man's mission take him?
a. Russia
b. Africa
c. South America

3. What type of ferocious reptiles chased Action Man Marine Mission?
a. Alligators
b. Iguanas
c. Snakes

4. Where did Action Man find Gangrene and Tempest?
a. Up in a tree house
b. Watching TV in Gangrene's house
c. At the bottom of the sea

5. Which form of transport did Tempest use to escape?
a. A bus
b. A train
c. A mini-sub

HOW YOU RATED:

5 answers correct: Well done! You have shown excellent agent skills.

2-4 answers correct: Not bad – with a little more practice and concentration you will eventually make the grade.

0-1 answer correct: Oh-oh! You'd better think of another career! You'd be an easy target for the Council of Doom.

Answers:1.b. 2.c. 3.a. 4.c. 5.c.

CADET TRAINING:2
CODES AND DECODING

A top special agent must be able to crack codes and read messages quickly – in order to ruin the bad guy's plans. Test your code cracking skills by trying to decipher each of the three messages on these pages. Check how you did on page 39.

Use the first letter of each animal or object in these pictures to decipher the message that Dr X has sent to Action Man. Write each letter in the box provided.

1	2	3	4	5	6	7	8	9	10	11	12
T	h	e		w	o	r	l	d	w	i	L

13	14	15	16	17	18	19	20	21	22
l	o	o	n	B	e		m	i	n

Match each symbol to the its corresponding letter – then you'll discover what Gangrene's message is all about. Write each letter in the space provided.

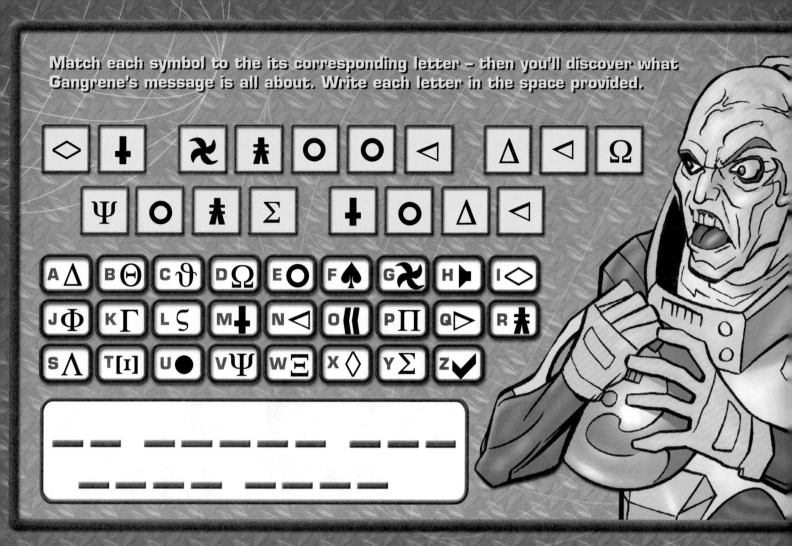

Match the final figure of each mathematical equation to its corresponding letter of the alphabet to figure out what's on Tempest's mind (eg. 2+2=4, 4=D). Write each letter in the space provided.

20+5= ☐ = ☐
30÷2= ☐ = ☐
7x3= ☐ = ☐

10+13= ☐ = ☐
11-2= ☐ = ☐
24÷2= ☐ = ☐
2x6= ☐ = ☐

10-4= ☐ = ☐
2x9= ☐ = ☐
16÷9= ☐ = ☐

CODE:

1=A	2=B	3=C	4=D	5=E
6=F	7=G	8=H	9=I	10=J

11=K	12=L	13=M	14=N
15=O	16=P	17=Q	18=R
19=S	20=T	21=U	22=V
23=W	24=X	25=Y	26=Z

CADET RATING: Record the number of codes that you deciphered correctly on page 109 – to find out your overall agent rating!

MISSION DATA:

MOUNTAIN MISSION!

MISSION BRIEF: *Dr X and Gangrene are now being held in prison on Demon's Island – but Tempest is still at large. We know he is operating in the mountains and he is harnessing electrical energy from storms to energise his electrical staff. Action Man will need the following equipment on this mission...*

SPECIAL OPERATION EQUIPMENT:

BODYSUIT
• Action Man's lifejacket has been specially made to fit him alone. It has thermal lining, which helps retain body temperature – even in the coldest conditions.

CANOE
• The body of the canoe is made from a top-secret, indestructible, lightweight fibreglass substance. The canoe's size and aerodynamic shape allows Action Man ultimate control in the water.

HEADGEAR
• The Mountain Mission helmet is made from toughened fibreglass – and reinforced with lightweight steel plates. It has a built in radio communication link and a navigational system plus a high-power spotlight is situated on the front.

FIREPOWER
• Two mini-missiles are positioned on either side of the canoe. Additional missiles are stored in the underside of the canoe. Missiles are accurate up to 3 miles.

MISSION LOCATION:
DRACONIAN MOUNTAIN RANGE, NORTH AMERICA
• HOME OF THE MOST DANGEROUS, MOUNTAINOUS WHITE WATER RAPIDS IN THE WORLD

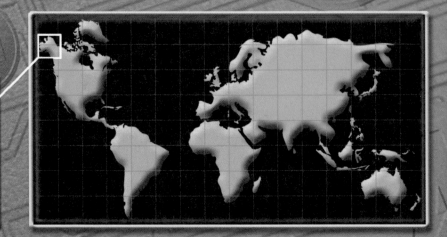

MISSION LOG: 11:20 HOURS. YOU'D THINK WITH DR X AND GANGRENE IN CUSTODY I'D BE ABLE TO TAKE IT EASY. NO SUCH LUCK.

I'M IN THE 'STONY RIDGE' MOUNTAIN RANGE - ONE OF THE MOST DANGEROUS PLACES IN THE WORLD.

REPORTS HAVE COME IN OF STRANGE LIGHTNING STORMS IN THIS VALLEY. IT DOESN'T TAKE A GENIUS TO FIGURE OUT WHO'S BEHIND IT.

LET'S GET THIS SHOW ON THE ROAD!

WHITE WATER - WHITE LIGHTNING!

GOTCHA!

KRR'ASSHH!

HE'S SO STILL. I'VE GOT TO SAVE HIM!

BUT IT'S NOT TEMPEST AT ALL. IT'S JUST A DUMMY.

AND NOW YOU'RE GONNA GET A PIECE OF THE REAL THING - ACTION MAN!

OH-OH! THIS DOESN'T LOOK GOOD - IT'S ONLY A FAKE!

IT WAS A TRAP THE WHOLE TIME!

OPERATION: RAPID FIRE!

When Action Man was making his way down the treacherous 'Stony Ridge' rapids he only had one thing on his mind. Take the first letter of all the things you can see on this page and write them in the boxes below – to reveal Action Man's inner-most thought.

1	2	3	4	5	6	7	8	9	10	11	12	13	14	15	16	17
I	M	U	S	T	C	A	T	C	H	T	E	M	P	E	S	T

50

MISSION DEBRIEF: WHITE WATER - WHITE LIGHTNING

Now is the time to test your special agent skills by trying to answer as many questions as possible about the preceding story: WHITE WATER - WHITE LIGHTNING. When you've finished, check your answers at the foot of this page. Then calculate your score to see how you have been rated by Action Man.

1. Where did Action Man's mission take place?
a. In the desert
b. In the mountains
c. In the city

2. How did Tempest create the rock-fall?
a. By barging the rocks with his canoe
b. Detonating an explosive
c. Firing his lightning rod at the rocks

3. Why did Tempest dive underwater?
a. To locate the next Keyhole to Infinity
b. To try and escape from Action Man
c. He just fancied a swim

4. How did Action Man knock the key from Tempest's hand?
a. With a karate kick
b. By using his canoe paddle
c. By throwing a rock at him

5. How was Tempest being transported to Demon's Island?
a. By ferry
b. By helicopter
c. By train

HOW YOU RATED:

5 answers correct: Top marks! Make sure you show the same concentration on the next mission.

2-4 answers correct: Good going! A little more concentration needed on the next mission though.

0-1 answer correct: C'mon now, it's time you pulled your socks up.

Answers: 1. b. 2. c. 3. a. 4. b. 5. b.

Make this superb Surveillance Tower for your Action Man and, when it's finished, he'll always be able to keep a watchful eye on the Council of Doom.

YOU WILL NEED:

2 sweet tubes (Smarties tubes are ideal), a tall cardboard box, several long strips of thin card, 3 to 5 old toothpaste boxes, large piece of corrugated card, ruler, safety scissors, masking tape, PVA glue, lots of old newspapers, poster paints.

TO MAKE THE TOWER:

1 Stand your cardboard box upright and make sure that Action Man can fit inside without his head touching the top. Now cut off the top and back panel of the box. Next, tape two empty sweet tubes together; this elongated tube will enable you to roll thin card into log shapes.

2 Measure the width of one side of the tower then cut a long strip of thin card to the same width. Now roll the card around the elongated tube (A). Mark a line where the card overlaps then remove the card and cut along the line. Now roll the same small piece of card around the tube again but this time tape the edges (B). Slide off the tube and you've made a log!

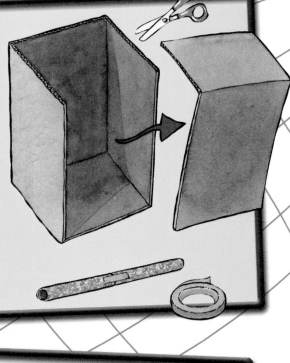

A

B

3 Repeat this process over and over again until you've made enough logs to cover all three side of the tower (don't forget to take new measurements for logs at the front of the tower.) Scrunch up small balls of newspaper and glue them into the end of each 'log'.

4 Stand your Action Man inside the tower and cut viewing hatches out of each tower side, at the correct height. Next, glue and tape the 'logs' into place on the outside of the tower.

PVA

5 Make two card supports for the roof by folding a strip of stiff card and tape each one into the front corners. Leave about 4cm sticking up from the top of the tower.

4 cm

6 Use a large piece of corrugated card to create the sloping roof. Cut it to size and angle it from the back of the tower up onto the raised roof supports. Now tape into place.

7 Place the tower onto a large, thick piece of card. Now place a small box beneath the rear of the tower and two sweet tubes (cut to the same height as the small box) beneath the front of the tower. Glue and tape the tubes and small box into place.

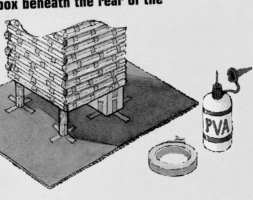

8 Use old toothpaste boxes (packed with newspaper and cut to size) to create steps that lead up into the rear of the tower.

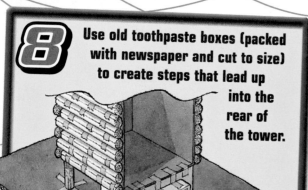

9 Now scrunch up old newspaper into balls and glue and stick them beneath and around the tower base so it looks as if the tower is perched on a rocky slope. Next, cover the entire thing in papier mache and leave to dry.

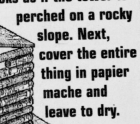

HOW TO PAINT:

Logs

Firstly, paint the logs brown. Once the paint is dry then use a fine brush to streak a deep brown, black or orange marking on logs, to create a wood effect. Paint the ends cream and when dry use a fine marker to draw the circular rings.

Roof

The corrugated card roof immediately gives the effect of corrugated iron. Try making it even more realistic by painting it a rusty red or even cover it with tin foil so it looks like new!

Interior

Paint the interior of the tower cream or light brown so it looks wooden on the inside. You can add posters and maps cut out from magazines and newspapers – or create your own!

Rocks

Use a sponge to dab the rocks with white, grey and black paint. Paint the steps the same way so they look as if they're carved out of the rock. You can add a splattering of green paint here and there so it looks like moss.

MISSION DATA:

WINDSURFER EXTREME!

MISSION BRIEF: *Reports are just coming in that there has been a perimeter breach on the maximum security prison on Demon's Island. Dr X, Gangrene and Tempest must be at the bottom of this disturbance. Action Man will need the following equipment on this mission...*

SPECIAL OPERATION EQUIPMENT:

HIGH-VELCOCITY ROCKETS

• Two sleek, reactor rockets are housed above the radar. Once a target is locked on via the radar – the rockets will hit home with 100 percent accuracy, over a 20 mile distance.

RADAR NAVIGATION SYSTEM

• The radar mounted at the front of the Windsurfer Extreme can pin-point a designated target, up to 2000 miles. It is coated with a top secret, anti-weathering agent - to keep it from the harsh, salty sea.

REINFORCED SAIL-FIN

• The tear-proof material used on the Windsurfer Extreme's sail-fin is able to cope with storm-force winds. The sail-fin can also be detached from the surfboard and used as an aerodynamic turbo speed sail – pulling Action Man along on his surfboard, just like a water-skier.

MISSION LOCATION:
DEMON'S ISLAND PRISON, NORTH PACIFIC OCEAN

• THE MOST SECURE JAIL IN THE WORLD – ONLY 'CATEGORY A' VILLAINS SPEND THEIR TIME HERE

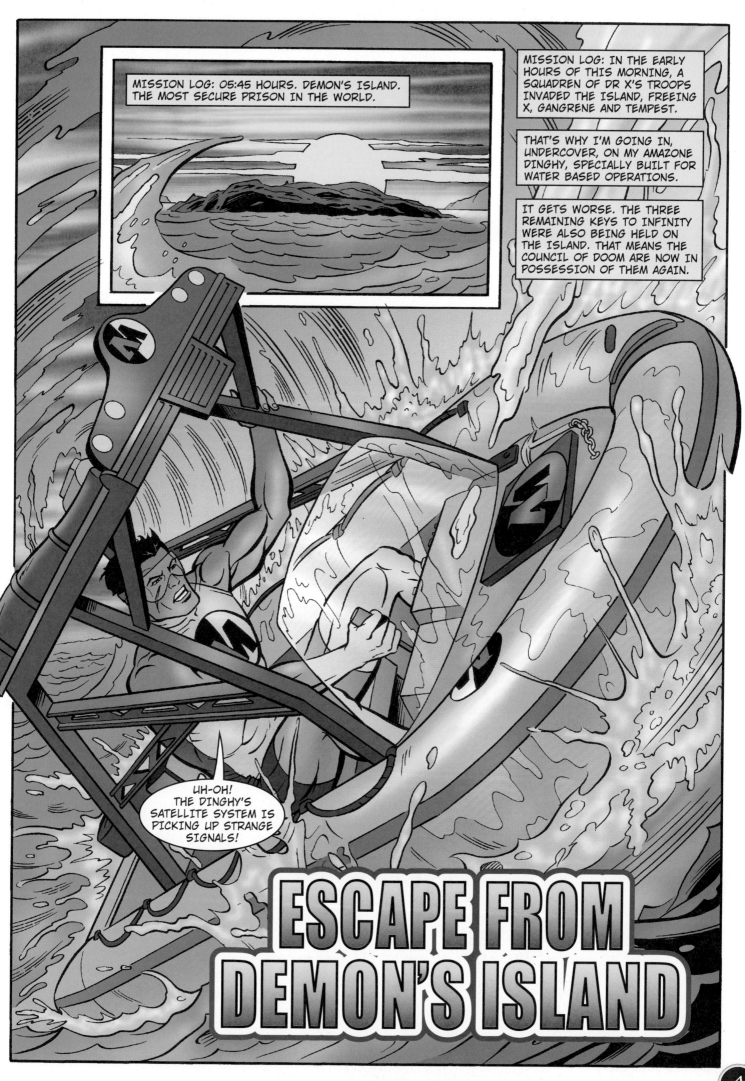

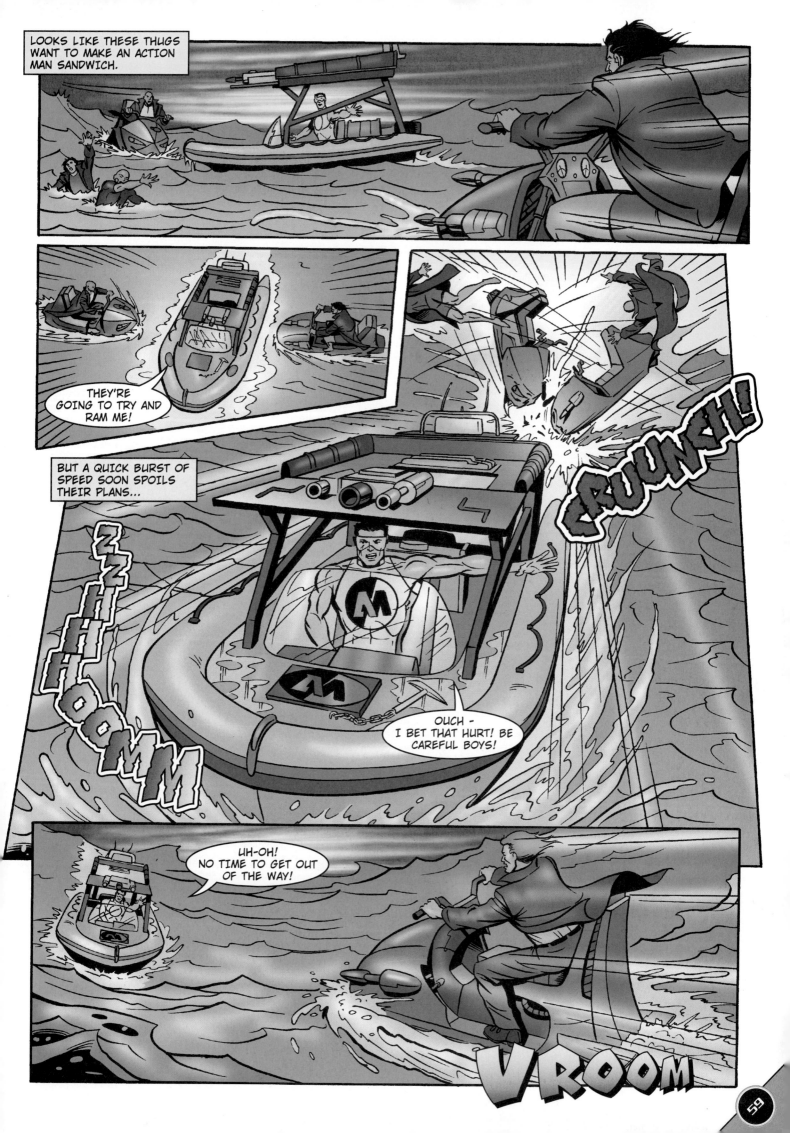

THE HULL OF THE DINGHY IS MADE OF A TOP SECRET, SUPER TOUGH RUBBER... THOSE WATER-BIKES ARE NO MATCH FOR IT!

KLONNKK

NOOOOOO!

I DIDN'T KNOW X'S THUGS COULD FLY!

I'LL HAVE TO CALL THE COASTGUARD TO PICK YOU GUYS UP. THERE'S ALREADY TOO MUCH POLLUTION IN THE OCEAN!

THERE IT IS, AT LAST - DEMON'S ISLAND. THINGS ARE ABOUT TO GET TOUGH!

MEANWHILE ON DEMON'S ISLAND, LET'S CATCH UP WITH THE COUNCIL OF DOOM.

THANK YOU, WARDEN. I BELIEVE THOSE KEYS BELONG TO ME!

YOU WON'T GET AWAY WITH THIS, X. ACTION MAN WILL SOON HAVE YOU BACK UNDER LOCK AND KEY!

THE STORY CONTINUES ON PAGE 73!

OPERATION: DOUBLE TROUBLE!

At first glance all these snapshot pictures of Windsurfer Extreme look exactly alike. But if you study them closely you will see that only 2 pictures are in fact, identical. Check them out and see how long it takes you to find the matching pair!

Action Man Pic (A)

Action Man Pic (B)

Action Man Pic (C)

Action Man Pic (D)

Action Man Pic (E)

Action Man Pic (F)

Action Man Pic (G)

Action Man Pic (H)

Action Man Pic (I)

Answers: B&I.

MISSION DEBRIEF: ESCAPE FROM DEMON'S ISLAND

Here's another chance for you to test your special agent skills. Try to answer as many questions as possible about the preceding story: **ESCAPE FROM DEMON'S ISLAND**. When you've finished, check your answers at the foot of this page. Then calculate your score and see how you have been rated by Action Man.

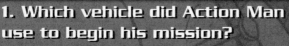

1. Which vehicle did Action Man use to begin his mission?
a. Amazone Dinghy
b. Arctic Surf Bike
c. Desert Buggy

2. How did Dr X's thugs attack Action Man?
a. On jet-skis
b. On a fishing boat
c. On boogie boards

3. Where on Demon's Island was the fourth Keyhole to Infinity?
a. In Dr X's cell
b. In a cave beneath the prison
c. In the prison governor's office

4. Which mode of transport did Action Man use to get inside the cave?
a. A skateboard
b. His Windsurfer Extreme
c. A scooter

5. How did the Council of Doom escape from Demon's Island?
a. On a raft
b. By helicopter
c. Aboard a Speedboat

HOW YOU RATED:

5 answers correct: You're the best! But being the best means that you have to keep up the good work on the next mission.

2-4 answers correct: Not bad at all! Just two mission debriefs left, and if you try a little harder, you're bound to improve!

0-1 answer correct: You've sunk without trace on this mission.

Answers:1.a. 2.a. 3.b. 4.b. 5.c.

67

CADET TRAINING:3
OBSERVATION AND JUDGEMENT

An elite special agent must rely on good observation skills and sound judgement in order to anticipate and confront the enemy. This is the final part of your cadet training. Solve the following puzzles then check your answers below..

FILE 1:

GONE TO PIECES!

This mystery villain is all in pieces. Draw each square, one by one, into the grid to reveal the bad guy's identity.

FILE 2: COUNTRY CONFUSION!

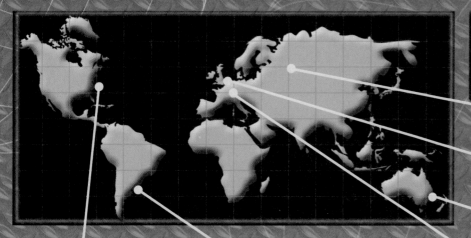

Dr X has major bases all over the world. Rearrange the letters to reveal the cities where his bases can be found.

CWOOMS

_ _ _ _ _ _

DNOOLN

_ _ _ _ _ _

ENW ROKY

_ _ _ _ _ _ _

ORI ED ANROEJI

_ _ _ _ _ _ _ _ _ _ _

RASIP

_ _ _ _ _

NEYSYD

_ _ _ _ _ _

FILE 3: SHADOW SHOW!

Take a look at all the silhouettes below – only one accurately matches Gangrene's pose. Can you tell which one it is?

1 2 3 4

FILE 4: BAD GUY LINE-UP!

There is only 1 true Dr X in this line up of bad guys – the rest are impostors. Can you tell who the real X is?

A B C D E F

6"
5"
4"
3"
2"

CADET RATING: Record the number of puzzles you answered correctly on page 109 – to find out your overall agent rating!

Answers:**FILE 1:** Tempest. **File 2:** 1. New York. 2. Rio de Janeiro. 3. Sydney. 4. London. 5. Paris. 6. Moscow. **FILE 3:** 3 **FILE 4:** The real Dr X is E.

69

PHOTO FINISH!

GANGRENE AND DR X HAVE BEEN CAUGHT ON CAMERA. USE YOUR SPECIAL AGENT ARTISTIC SKILLS TO REPRODUCE A DRAWING OF EACH BAD GUY IN THE GRIDS PROVIDED.

SNOWBALL MOBILE FIRE!

SPECIAL OPERATION EQUIPMENT:

SNOWBALL MISSILES

• As the Snowball Mobile speeds along, snow is sucked up then condensed into huge balls and stored in the launching chambers. Snowball missiles can be fired accurately over a distance of 800 meters.

HIGH IMPACT JET-SKIS

• Two high impact mini skis sit beneath the front of the Snowball Mobile – allowing Action Man better vision. State-of-the-art suspension gives a comfortable ride over the roughest of terrains. The rear of the vehicle is powered by super-charged, snow-chain traction treads.

ALL-WEATHER VISOR

• Microscopic heaters are embedded into the visor. Even in the coldest of conditions, the visor will remain crystal clear. It also has a night-vision mode – allowing full visibility in the dead of night.

MISSION BRIEF: *Strange happenings are occurring in the small Siberian village of Krinkov. An invading army has descended on the village – and the Council of Doom have also been sighted close by. Action Man will need to use the following equipment on this mission...*

MISSION LOCATION:

KRINKOV, SIBERIA

• PROBABLY ONE OF THE COLDEST AND DESOLATE PLACES ON THE PLANET

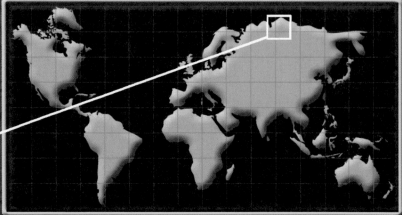

COSSACK FURY

MISSION LOG: 16:32 HOURS. REPORTS JUST IN - THE INHABITANTS OF THE SIBERIAN VILLAGE OF KRINKOV HAVE BEEN DRIVEN FROM THEIR HOMES BY AN INVADING ARMY OF... COSSACKS?!

YAH! FLEE! DOGS! RUN FOR YOUR PUNY LIVES!

RUN AWAY! THE COSSACKS ARE COMING!

THE RUSSIAN AUTHORITIES HAVE ASKED FOR MY HELP.

DR X AND HIS GANG HAVE BEEN TOO QUIET FOR TOO LONG. THIS MUST HAVE SOMETHING TO DO WITH THEM!

THE AIRCRAFT DROPS ME IN THE MIDDLE OF NOWHERE, 30KM FROM THE VILLAGE OF KRINKOV...

...GOOD JOB I'VE GOT MY SNOWBALL MOBILE!

OPERATION: COLD CLIMATE!

Before Action Man was sent out on his mission to Siberia, he decided to pack a bag full of essential accessories. Take a look at all the garments and objects below and identify which 5 items Action Man chose not to take on this chilly mission.

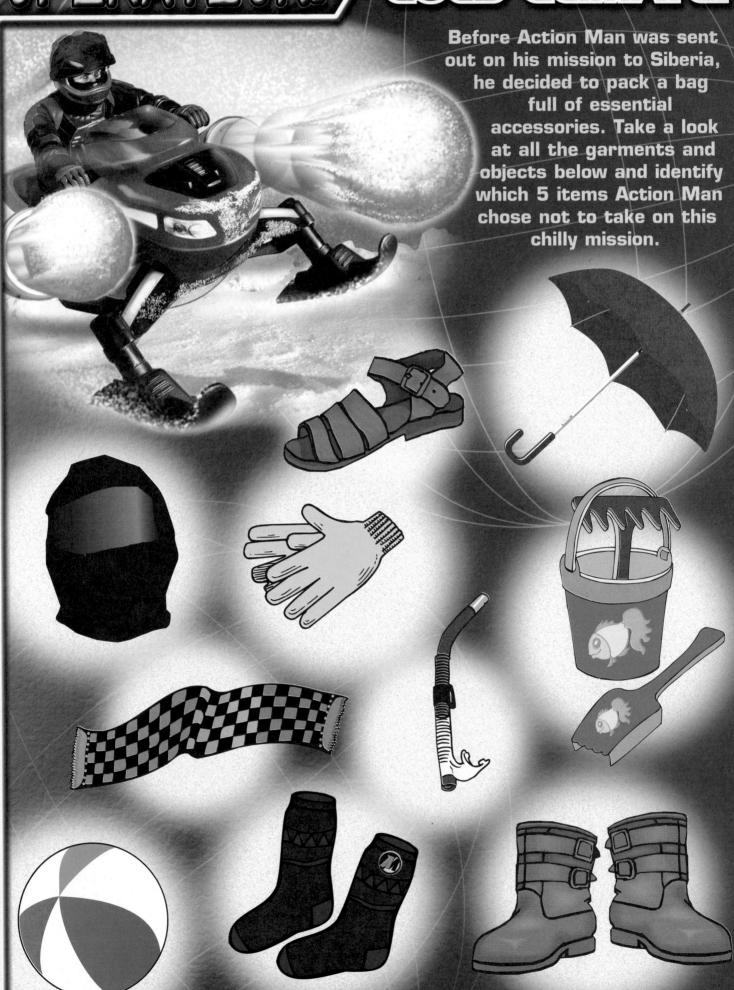

MISSION DEBRIEF: COSSACK FURY

Test your special agent skills by trying to answer as many questions as possible about the preceding story: **COSSACK FURY**. When you've finished. check your answers at the foot of this page. Then calculate your score to see how you have been rated by Action Man.

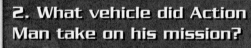

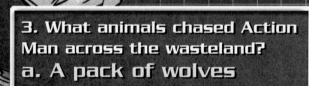

1. Where did Action Man's mission take place?
a. Jamaica
b. Africa
c. Siberia

2. What vehicle did Action Man take on his mission?
a. Skateboard Extreme
b. Snowball Mobile Fire
c. Kart Extreme

3. What animals chased Action Man across the wasteland?
a. A pack of wolves
b. A herd of buffalo
c. A flock of seagulls

4. What was the Council of Doom up to in the forest?
a. Camping
b. Holding a party
c. Melting the snow to discover a treasure chest

5. How does Action Man knock the casket out of X's grasp?
a. He fires a catapult
b. He uses one of his snowball missiles
c. He fires an arrow from a bow

HOW YOU RATED:

5 answers correct: Top marks! You really are showing great potential to eventually become a top agent.

2-4 answers correct: Good – now show more concentration and one last effort in the final mission to improve your score.

0-1 answer correct: Not very good at all! If you had to face the Council of Doom – you'd have no chance.

Answers:1. c. 2. b. 3. a. 4. c. 5. b.

81

BAD T'O

Ha-ha! So you wanna be a member of the Council of Doom, eh? Well first you've gotta prove yourself! Complete these puzzles and tasks – then we'll let you know if you've made the grade!

TASK 1

PICTURE PERFECT!

Draw this picture of little ol' me from one grid into the other! Draw it well – or your application will be cancelled straightaway! Ha-ha!

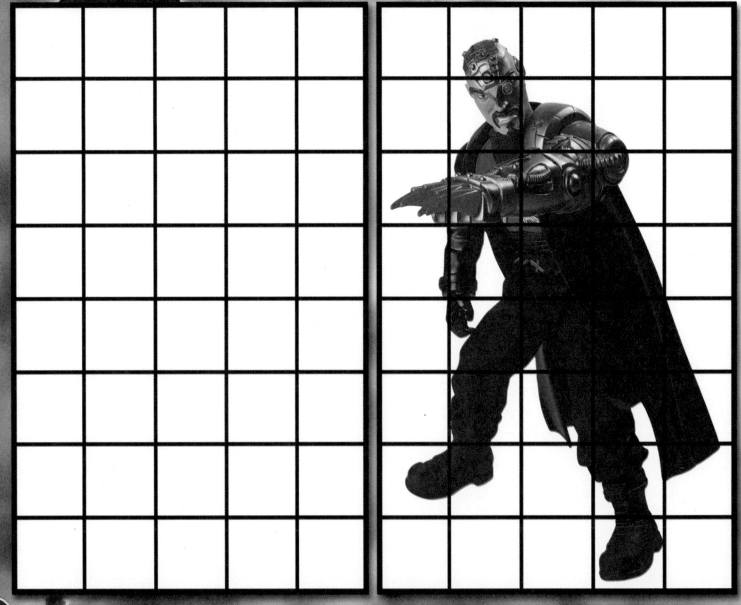

THE BONE!

TASK 2

SHOCK, HORROR!

I have only one message for Action Man – d'you wanna know what it is? Then follow my electrical energy beam, connecting each letter and you'll soon find out!

E L Z
A S I Z
C L I W
T I L L A
O N M N

Answer: The message should read, ACTION MAN WILL SIZZLE!

TASK 3

TOXIC TERROR!

Heh-heh! In the past, these six countries have all experienced my toxic terror! Fit their names into the crossword grid and, when complete, the shaded area will reveal one of my most favourite things!

Libya

Denmark

United States   Greece

Switzerland   England

Answer: Gangrene's favourite thing is... 'SLUDGE!'

FREEFALL FRENZY!

Ha! I'll bounce back from this little tumble – just you wait and see! Now give this picture some colour – and make it lightning fast!

THAT'S TORN IT!!

Grrr! Someone has shredded photos from my Action Man classified collection. Only one picture cannot be completed – which one is it?

Answer: Picture 2 cannot be completed.

SIGNING OFF!

Have you made it into the Council of Doom? See what Tempest, Gangrene and Dr X have to say...

0-2 TASKS COMPLETED

I LIKED YOUR LIGHTNING QUICK REACTIONS, KID! YOU SEEM LIKE A REAL LIVEWIRE! BUT I JUST DON'T THINK YOU'VE GOT THAT CERTAIN 'SPARK' THAT'S NEEDED TO JOIN OUR ELITE GANG! HEH-HEH!

3-4 TASKS COMPLETED

HEY, KID! NOT BAD! BUT I BET YOU COULDN'T MIX A TOXIC POTION THAT'S STRONG ENOUGH TO DISSOLVE A BUS, EH?! HA! I THOUGHT NOT! WE NEED PROFESSIONALS - NOT AMATEURS!

ALL 5 TASKS COMPLETED

HMMM! OKAY, SO YOU MANAGED TO SOLVE ALL THE PUZZLES AND COMPLETE THE TASKS WE SET FOR YOU - BIG DEAL! THE COUNCIL OF DOOM DOESN'T NEED ANY MORE MEMBERS - SO THERE! HA-HA!

MISSION DATA:

VERTICAL MISSION!

MISSION BRIEF: *While London's top scientists are trying to open a small, ancient casket – which looks like it could be the final 'Keyhole to Infinity', the Council of Doom are still on the loose. Be extra vigilant – they could attack at any moment!*

SPECIAL OPERATION EQUIPMENT:

AUTO-WINCHING LEVER

• Action Man only needs to push the lever forwards and a ratchet effect mechanism propels him up the abseiling rope. Pulling the lever back allows Action Man to slide downwards.

COMMUNICATIONS HEADSET

• This lightweight communications headset is attached around Action Man's ear and allows him direct contact with HQ.

MISSILE LAUNCH

• Attached to the Vertical Mission winching system is Action Man's lightweight missile launcher. Telescopic sights allow the missile to be 'locked on' to any designated target.

MISSION LOCATION:

HIGHGROVE RESEARCH CENTRE, LONDON

• SOME OF THE WORLD'S TOP SCIENTIFIC MINDS CARRY OUT THEIR OBSERVATIONS AT THIS SECURE UNIT

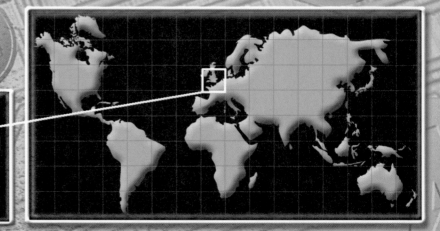

SHLAP!

MAKE WAY - 'COS I'M COMING ON THROUGH!

DONNK!

GUHHHH!

DOOOHHHH!

ACTION MAN IS IN THE BUILDING - DESTROY HIM!

RIGHT AWAY!

YES, SIR!

RIGHT, GOING UP!

SORRY GUYS AND GOONS, BUT YOU'RE GONNA HAVE TO MAKE WAY!

COLOUR EXTREME

Make a jump for your colouring pens and give Action Man Vertical Mission a splash of colour.

OPERATION: SIGNING OFF!

Action Man has received one final message on his laptop computer, from the Council of Doom. However, parts of the message do not make sense. From the options provided, insert the correct words to complete the Council of Doom's final notice to Action Man.

TO ACTION MAN

OKAY, TOUGH ¹_____ ! SO YOU MANAGED TO ²_____ US THIS TIME - BIG ³_____ ! BUT WE'LL BE BACK ⁴_____ WITH ANOTHER ⁵_____ - THEN THE WORLD WILL BE ⁶_____ !

THE COUNCIL OF ⁷_____ !

¹ PIE / FLY / GUY
² TREAT / BEAT / FEET
³ DEAL / FEEL / STEAL
⁴ SPOON / SOON / BABOON
⁵ POT / PET / PLOT
⁶ OURS / FLOWERS / SHOWERS
⁷ BLOOM / DOOM / GLOOM

MISSION DEBRIEF: SUMMIT OF DOOM

This is your final chance to test your special agent skills by trying to answer as many questions as possible about the preceding story: **SUMMIT OF DOOM**. When you've finished, check your answers at the foot of this page. Then calculate your score to see how you have been rated by Action Man.

1. Where was the research centre called 'Summit Towers' situated?
a. Moscow
b. Paris
c. London

2. How did Action Man get onto the roof of Summit Towers?
a. By parachuting
b. Dropped in by helicopter
c. By glider

3. What essential piece of equipment did Action Man use on this mission?
a. Vertical Mission
b. Arctic Rally Car
c. Marine Mission

4. When Dr X escaped to his helicopter, what did he carry underneath his arm?
a. The final Keyhole to Infinity
b. His shopping
c. A newspaper

5. How is the case which holds the final Keyhole to Infinity destroyed?
a. Dr X drops it
b. It's run over by a bus
c. Action Man blasts it with a missile

HOW YOU RATED:

5 answers correct: A perfect score and excellent performance - you've shown all the qualities to become a top secret agent.

2-4 answers correct: You haven't far to go to improve. Keep training hard - you could still make it as a top agent.

0-1 answer correct: The life of a special agent certainly isn't for you.

Answers:1. c. 2. b. 3. a. 4. a. 5. c.

THE FINAL WORD!

Now the world can rest in peace, safe in the knowledge that the Council of Doom are locked up behind bars! But as usual, these three bad guys want to have the last word!

DR. X

A statement from the evil Dr X

' Action Man – you think that you are so smart. But mere bars cannot contain me and I'll be back with a vengeance - just you wait and see! The Council of Doom WILL be back very soon!'

001245362–X

PROF. GANGRENE

A statement from the grubby Gangrene

' When I get out of this prison I'm gonna make the most smelliest toxic potion ever – especially for one person – that interfering Action Man! Heh-heh!'

001245999-G

TEMPEST

A statement from the electrifying Tempest

' I just wanna have one chance of frazzling that no good do-gooder, Action Man! And once I get a clear shot at him, he'll fry like a sausage!'

001245583-T